For Tom Ellen

First published 1985 by Walker Books Ltd
87 Vauxhall Walk, London SE11 5HJ

This edition published 2001

2 4 6 8 10 9 7 5 3 1

© 1985 Shirley Hughes

This book has been typeset in Vendome

Printed in Hong Kong

British Library Cataloguing in Publication Data:
a catalogue record for this book
is available from the British Library

ISBN 0-7445-6986-9

Bathwater's Hot

Shirley Hughes

WALKER BOOKS
AND SUBSIDIARIES
LONDON · BOSTON · SYDNEY

Bathwater's hot,

Seawater's cold,

Ginger's kittens are *very* young

But Buster's getting old.

Some things you can throw away,

Some are nice to keep.

Here's someone who is wide awake,

Shhh, he's fast asleep!

Some things are hard as stone,
Some are soft as cloud.

Whisper very quietly ...

SHOUT OUT LOUD!

It's fun to run very fast

Or to be slow.

The red light says "stop"

And the green light says "go".

It's kind to be helpful,

Unkind to tease,

Rather rude to push and grab,

Polite to say "please".

Night time is dark,

Day time is light.

The sun says "good morning"

And the moon says "good night".

W A L ... K S

The Nursery Collection

SHIRLEY HUGHES says that she found working on The Nursery Collection "very stimulating". They were her first books for very young children and she remarks that creating them was "concentrated and exhausting because it was like actually being with a very small child." The brother and sister featured in the books reappear in her book of seasonal verse *Out and About* and in a series of books about "doing words" – *Bouncing*, *Chatting*, *Giving* and *Hiding* – now collected in a single volume as *Let's Join In*.

Shirley Hughes has won numerous awards, including the Kate Greenaway Medal for *Dogger* and the Eleanor Farjeon Award for services to children's literature. In 1999 she was awarded the OBE. Among her many popular books are the *Alfie and Annie Rose*, *Lucy and Tom* and *Tales of Trotter Street* series.

Shirley and her husband, a retired architect, have lived in the same house in west London for more than forty years. They have three grown-up children and six grandchildren.

ISBN 0-7445-6983-4 (pb)   ISBN 0-7445-6986-9 (pb)   ISBN 0-7445-6984-2 (pb)   ISBN 0-7445-6981-8 (pb)   ISBN 0-7445-6985-0 (pb)   ISBN 0-7445-6982-6 (pb)